Raintree is an imprint of Capstone Global Library Limited, a company incorporated in England and Wales having its registered office at 7 Pilgrim Street, London, EC4V 6LB - Registered company number: 6695582

To contact Raintree please phone 0845 6044371, fax +44 (0) 1865 312263, or email myorders@raintreepublishers.co.uk.
Customers from outside the UK please telephone +44 1865 312262.

Originally published by DC Comics in the U.S. in single magazine form as Superman Adventures #6.
Copyright © 2013 DC Comics. All Rights Reserved.

DC Comics
1700 Broadway, New York, NY 10019
A Warner Bros. Entertainment Company

First published by Stone Arch Books in 2013
First published in the United Kingdom in 2014
The moral rights of the proprietor have been asserted.

Ashley C. Andersen Zantop *Publisher*
Michael Dahl *Editorial Director*
Donald Lemke & Sean Tulien *Editors*
Heather Kindseth *Creative Director*
Bob Lentz *Designer*
Kathy McColley *Production Specialist*

DC COMICS
Mike McAvennie *Original US Editor*
Rick Burchett & Terry Austin *Cover Artists*

Originated by Capstone Global Library Ltd
Printed and bound in China by Leo Paper Products Ltd

ISBN 978 1 406 26681 8
17 16
10 9 8 7 6 5 4 3 2

British Library Cataloguing in Publication Data
A full catalogue record for this book is available from the British Library.

SUPERMAN ADVENTURES

Seanimod

Scott McCloud .... writer
Rick Burchett .... penciller
Terry Austin .... inker
Marie Severin .... colourist
Lois Buhalis .... letterer

Superman created by
Jerry Siegel & Joe Shuster

6

"TOO MANY PEOPLE AND NO TIME, I HAD ONLY *ONE* OPTION."

BUMDH!

COUGH! COUGH!

"NOW I WAS *ANGRY*."

STOP HIM, MY *BROTHERS!* I MUST REACH THE *ESCAPE VEHICLE* AND OUR *SECRET WEAPON!*

URI, YOU *IDIOT!* I *TOLD* YOU WE SHOULD HAVE BROUGHT IT *WITH* US!

SO WHAT WAS THE "SECRET WEAPON," CLARK?

JONATHAN! YOU LET HIM TELL IT AT HIS OWN PACE! ANYWAY, I'M SURE WE CAN *GUESS* WHAT IT WAS.

OH, I DON'T THINK *YOU* CAN GUESS WHAT HAPPENED *NEXT*, MA.

I *LIVED* THROUGH IT, AND I CAN *STILL* HARDLY BELIEVE IT.

14

15

SO WAS MXYZPTLK TRYING TO HELP OR NOT? I DON'T GET IT..WHAT DID HE STAND TO GAIN?

MXYZPTLK NEVER EXACTLY *HELPS*, PA, THOUGH THIS TIME HE WAS HELPING ME LEARN SOMETHING VERY IMPORTANT.

HE HAS A PRETTY NASTY STREAK, THOUGH.

HOW IS IT YOU GET RID OF HIM, DEAR? I FORGET. DO YOU MAKE HIM SAY HIS NAME TWICE?

TWICE *BACKWARDS*. I REMEMBER THAT PART.

"*EXACTLY!* ALTHOUGH AT THE TIME THAT WAS THE FURTHEST THING FROM MY MIND. I WAS TOO BUSY FIGURING OUT WHAT WENT WRONG WITH THAT *JET.*"

AH, DON'T WORRY. KIDS JUST PARANOID.

I GUESS IT'S NOTHING.

THE SERGEANT WILL TELL US IF THERE'S ANYTHING WRONG.

MAYBE THESE TWO CAN GIVE US SOME CLUES.

"INSIDE A SMALL ON-DECK OFFICE, TWO MEN SEEMED UPSET ABOUT TWO DIFFERENT THINGS."

18

HMMM... LET'S SEE WHAT CAUSED THE JAM-UP...

FACE IT, SUPE--YOU'RE A *FISH OUTTA WATER!* YOU'RE *DROWNIN'* OUT HERE! GIVE UP, ALREADY!

"AS THE TRAFFIC CLEARED, I SAW TWO BLOCKS DOWN TO THE SOURCE OF THE JAM, AN ACCIDENT.

"A *FATAL* ACCIDENT."

"SUDDENLY, THE DRIVER'S HEAD *SNAPPED UP,* AND THE CAR PULLED BACK-WARDS AND *RE-FORMED* ITSELF.

"THEN IT SWERVED BACK AND RESUMED ITS NORMAL COURSE. AND FINALLY, I SAW THE CAUSE OF THE ACCIDENT--

"--A YOUNG BOY, NOT TEN YEARS OLD, RUNNING ACROSS THE STREET."

THEN *THIS* IS WHERE IT ALL BEGAN!

"WHERE IT ALL BEGAN"? IT ALL BEGAN WITH A BIG BANG, STUPID!

BUT, YEAH, THIS IS THE SOURCE OF ALL YOUR HEADACHES.

BUT *WHY* DID HE RUN OUT INTO THE STREET?

HEY, STUPID!

OF COURSE!

BUT WHY DID THE OTHER BOY LET THE BALL GO PAST HIM?

"THEN I DISCOVERED NOT ONLY WHAT HAD DISTRACTED HIM...

BOOM!

"...BUT ALSO WHAT THE TERRORISTS' TARGET HAD BEEN--

BONG!

"--THE OLD METROPOLIS CLOCK TOWER."

20

"*I* KNEW, AND THAT WAS ENOUGH. AND LATER, WHEN THE CROWDS AND POLICE LEFT AND IT WAS JUST ME AND THE CITY..."

"...IT SURE FELT GOOD TO WATCH THE SUN REFLECTING OFF THE BEAUTIFUL SKYSCRAPERS OF METROPOLIS, AND TO FEEL THAT GREAT SURGE OF HUMANITY MOVING FORWARD AND LOOKING AHEAD--"

"--TO THE *FUTURE* ONCE MORE."

END

SCOTT McCLOUD WRITER

Scott McCloud is an acclaimed comics creator and author whose best-known work is the graphic novel *Understanding Comics*. His work also includes the science-fiction adventure series *Zot!*, a 12-issue run of *Superman Adventures*, and much more. Scott is the creator of the "24 Hour Comic", and frequently lectures on comics theory.

RICK BURCHETT PENCILLER

Rick Burchett has worked as a comics artist for more than 25 years. He has received the comics industry's Eisner Award three times, Spain's Haxtur Award, and he has been nominated for the Eagle Award in the UK. Rick lives with his wife and two sons in Missouri, USA.

TERRY AUSTIN INKER

Throughout his career, inker Terry Austin has received dozens of awards for his work on high-profile comics for DC Comics and Marvel, such as *The Uncanny X-Men*, *Doctor Strange*, *Justice League America*, *Green Lantern*, and *Superman Adventures*. He lives in New York, USA.

anarchy chaos, or a state of society without government or law

crusade fight against something considered wrong or evil

debris scattered pieces of something that has been broken or destroyed

detonation the action of causing a bomb to explode

fascist person who has extreme views and wants to control others

glimpsed saw something very briefly

malfunction fail to work properly

melodrama overly emotional, unreasonable manner of behaviour

nuisance someone or something that annoys you and causes problems

underestimate think that something is less important than it really is

receding moving back or fading gradually

surveyed looked at the whole of a scene or situation, often to make a plan

tragedy sad or shocking event

SUPERMAN GLOSSARY

Clark Kent: Superman's alter ego, Clark Kent, is a reporter for the *Daily Planet* newspaper and was raised by Jonathan and Martha Kent. No one knows he is Superman except for his adopted parents, the Kents.

The Daily Planet: the city of Metropolis's biggest and most read newspaper. Clark, Lois, Jimmy, and Perry all work for the *Daily Planet.*

Invulnerability: Superman's invulnerability makes him impervious to harm. Almost nothing can hurt him -- except for Kryptonite.

The Kent Family: Jonathan and Martha Kent found Superman when he crashed to Earth from his home planet, Krypton. They raised him as their own child, giving him the name Clark.

Krypton: the planet where Superman was born. Brainiac destroyed Krypton shortly after Superman's parents sent him on his way to Earth.

Kryptonite: a radioactive rock from Superman's home planet, Krypton.

Metropolis: the city where Clark Kent (Superman) lives.

Mxyzptlk: a magical, mischievous imp from the Fifth Dimension. Mxy can only be defeated by tricking him into saying his name backwards twice.

The Fifth Dimension: an inter-dimensional reality. Due to its five-dimensional properties, this reality has a different set of physics than ours. It is also the home world of a race of impish beings who are able to alter their dimensions as a form of magic.

VISUAL QUESTIONS & PROMPTS

1. Do you think Mxy is evil, or just a playful trickster? Why? Explain your answer using specific illustrations from this comic book.

2. What happened between these two panels (from page 22)? How did the first panel lead into the second one?

3. Below, in the third panel, the baseball passes the panel's border. Why do you think the creators of this comic did that?

4 This panel has little lines coming out from Mxy's head. How does Mxy feel in this shot? What do you think those lines mean?

5 Why do the sound effects read backwards in this panel? Read through this section of the comic book again, then explain your answer using details.

6 Why was it important for Superman to catch the baseball? Explain why he went to such great effort to catch it.